A Read-Together Book for Parents and Children

CREATED IN COOPERATION WITH THE MENNINGER FOUNDATION

Look at Me Now!

by

JANE WERNER WATSON

ROBERT E. SWITZER, M.D.
Director of the Children's Division
The Menninger Clinic

J. COTTER HIRSCHBERG, M.D.
Associate Director of the Children's Division
The Menninger Clinic

Illustrated by

HILDE HOFFMANN

The Dorothy Wright Treatment and Endowment Fund
defrays a part of the care and treatment cost at the
Children's Division of The Menninger Clinic,
Box 829, Southard Place, Topeka, Kansas 66601.
Part of the income from the sale
of this book goes to that fund.

GOLDEN PRESS • NEW YORK

WESTERN PUBLISHING COMPANY, INC.

Racine, Wisconsin

NOTE TO PARENTS:

Most children who are two years old, or thereabouts, are fascinated with themselves, their rapidly increasing abilities and their widening horizons. They wonder how they grew to where they are now. This book will help you and your child recall with pleasure and satisfaction all that has been accomplished. Looking back on the process of growth and learning will help the child feel more comfortable about all the change and learning that lies ahead.

As you review your two-year-old's experiences, it is clear that from the start there were things that were difficult and other things that were easy. Some activities were fun; others were frustrating. All were important.

Months The new baby's existence has inborn pattern.

0-3 Gradually, sleeping and being awake and eating take on a routine. Sometimes the world feels good to the baby; at other times it feels bad. One very important source of security is learning to recognize Mother's face—at first just as an oval with two eyes. There is also the awareness that feeling good is related to Mother. When Baby is hungry, Mother feeds him. When he is cold, she makes him warm and dry. When the world isn't right, she cuddles and soothes him and makes reassuring sounds that are warm and friendly.

Mother and Father cannot keep the baby from feeling

hurt or angry or cold. But when the baby has learned that hurt can go away, that cold can turn to warmth, he has made a long step toward growing up.

Months 3-6 Gradually, Baby learns that he and his mother are separate people. She can go away, but she always comes back, and he can remember the good feeling of her presence even while she is not there. His concept of himself as a separate person is added to by his increasing ability to exercise motor control—grasping, kicking, pushing. He begins to respond to Mother with gestures and to play little games with movements of his own. He recognizes and remembers parts of his crib and his bath toys. When a new, strange toy is added, he decides whether to accept it or to push it away. Similarly with his food he begins to like or dislike the taste of things, in addition to having the earlier pleasant feeling of being full. Certain movements and sounds have become familiar. He likes to repeat them and have them repeated for him.

Months 6-9 Baby and his parents now communicate in new and different ways. Tired sounds, hungry sounds, angry, painful, contented and happy sounds take on new meanings. Baby adapts to what he can see and hear in terms of what he has learned. He responds more actively, pushing against things as well as holding on. Teething lets him bite as well as suck, chomp as well as swallow. He can inflict pain and see the reaction.

His world expands as he sits up, creeps, pulls himself up and explores. If he is encouraged to move about and investigate, with only protective interference, he will feel that his learning has value. He explores his own body, playing with his own ears, nose, fingers, penis and toes. New sounds interest him, and he makes new voice noises.

Mother remains the most important figure in his world, but being assured of her love and support he can let her out of sight and hold her in his mind. The excitement and reassurance of playing "peek-a-boo" lies in this. As he develops new ways of making contact with Mother, he becomes less dependent on the breast and bottle, and so prepares himself for weaning.

Sometimes as the eighth and ninth month are reached, and Baby can accept Mother's absence more readily, he needs help in getting used to new people. It is a normal part of growing up that new people can frighten him even though they didn't when he was younger. He needs help from Mother and Father to learn through gradual introductions that strangers can become pleasurable.

Months Mother and Father now see in the baby the be-
9-12 ginning of sequences of reasonable thoughts, judgments and decisions. He is able to delay gratification and to anticipate it. He starts to show recogni-

tion of cause and effect. He responds to behavioral cues, especially "no" from Mother. The baby's style in these matters begins to reflect his individuality.

Baby's world is enlarging as he increasingly is able to interpret things he sees and hears at a distance. Close at hand, he is sensitive to the moods and responses of his parents. He tries out what effect he can have, and what he can resist. Sharing of experiences can lead to increasing pleasure for both. But the baby can feel fear, anger and jealousy as well as sympathy and affection. He can recognize these feelings and moods in others, and he responds.

By the end of the first year the baby sits alone comfortably and probably stands. He shows pleasure and displeasure, not yet in words but in very meaningful ways. He reaches out and pulls back, communicates with Mother, and expresses awareness of others.

Months **12-18** The infant now takes pleasure in learning to walk and in converting jargon into simple word symbols. There is a rapid increase in understanding of words, and in communicating by gestures and sounds. He learns to climb, handle things, fill and empty, and to bang! He cooperates in being dressed, learns to take off his shoes and socks—but cannot possibly put them back on! He begins to establish a hand preference (right or left) and tries to feed himself.

He begins to question and to have a concept of relative time, mealtime, naptime, and so on. "What is that?" "Daddy home soon?" and other questions display his growing vocabulary and awareness. Still, he cannot deal comfortably with being apart from Mother for long. He has little knowledge of danger and needs constant protection.

Months 18-24 Potty training comes along at around a year and a half. This gives Baby his first experience of direct control over Mother. He can please her or he can please himself, give or stubbornly withhold, defy or choose the reward of approval. Along with this power comes new self-assertiveness. "I can do it myself." He teases, begins to show humor and also open affection. He is possessive, likes to give orders. But he also begins to have a capacity to feel sorry and to have a sense of shame at a lack of accomplishment. In general he likes to co-operate and conform. New experiences and variety are taken in stride, especially when they increase his secure sense of himself. He likes sitting down with his parents to have them read to him a book like this about himself, so that he can think with them about himself as "I."

Robert E. Switzer

Robert E. Switzer, M.D.
Director of Children's Division
THE MENNINGER CLINIC

J. Cotter Hirschberg, M.D.

J. Cotter Hirschberg, M.D.
Associate Director of Children's Division
THE MENNINGER CLINIC

Look at Me Now!

Once there was a new baby.
It couldn't do much.
It slept most of the time.

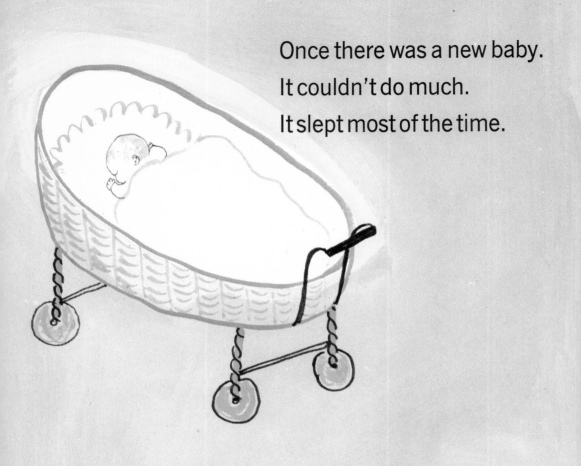

When it was awake
it just stuck out its tongue
and blew spit bubbles.

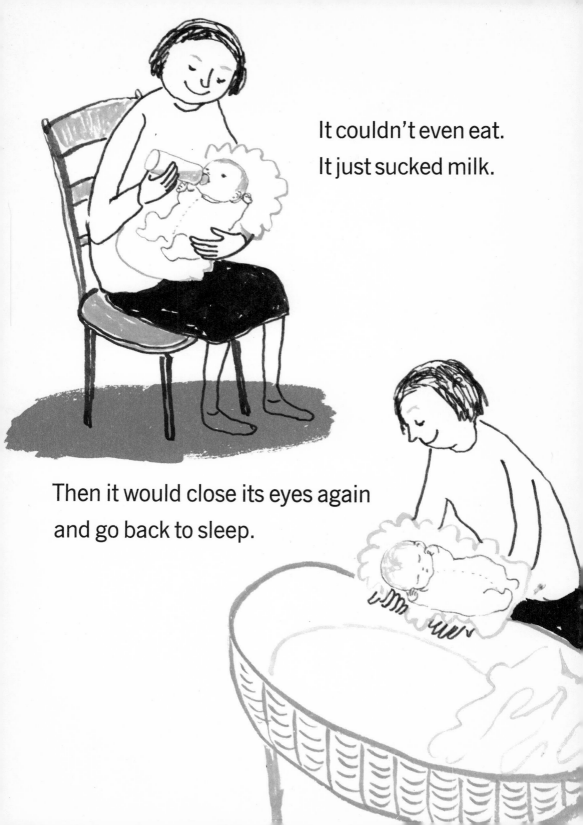

It couldn't even eat.
It just sucked milk.

Then it would close its eyes again
and go back to sleep.

Do you know what?
I was that baby!
It was long, long ago, of course.
Just **look at me now!**

When I was a new baby,
I couldn't understand sounds I heard.
I couldn't understand what I saw.
I couldn't talk.

But I could cry.
I cried when I was hungry,
or hot, or cold, or wet.
Sometimes I cried just because
I wanted to be held close.

Little by little
I learned to tell nice,
soft sounds

from sharp, scary ones.

I learned to look at things around me
and recognize them.
I knew my mother and my father.

I could hold on with my hands.
I could kick with my feet.
I began to roll over and move around.

Of course, I don't really remember that time.

It was long ago, as you can see.

Just **look at me now!**

When I'd been here about half a year,
I began to grow teeth.
That hurt and made me cross.

I chewed a lot
and learned to bite!

There was so much to learn —
all about myself from hair to toes.
It was fun to play with those.

I learned to sit up

and to creep.

I learned to pull myself up

until I could almost stand alone.

But just **look at me now!**

As I grew a little bit older,

I learned to handle things.

I knew which foods I liked best.

I could make different sounds.

Then I could say "coo" and "maa maa."

But just **listen to me now!**

Mother began to leave me
alone sometimes to play.

But we played together, too.

I saw other people
more and more.
I wasn't sure
if I liked them.

I could tell Mother things,
like "All gone."

I liked to try to do new things,
and Mother let me try.

But I knew what it meant
when Mother said, "No, no!"

As I grew bigger,

I liked to have my own way.

I didn't always want to be dressed.

I didn't always want to be clean.

I learned to hit and kick.

But when Mother or Daddy scolded,
I was unhappy.
I liked to have them pleased with me,
even when I was still small.

I learned to welcome
people I liked.

I was sorry when they left.

Well, I kept growing bigger and stronger.
I learned to creep upstairs —

to climb —

to push doors —
and to put things together.

I learned
to wave "Bye bye!" —

to play by myself —
and to let Mother know
when I was wet, afterward.

But **look at me now!**

Now there is so much that I can do.

I tell Mother when I want to go to potty.

I like being dry and clean.

I can take off my own shoes
and socks.

I can play with toys
and blocks.

I like my own favorite toys.

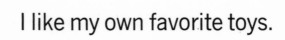

I like to hug and kiss.

I like to look at books like this.

I like to look at little babies
and think
I was once a little baby too.
But look at me,
look at me now!